IN THE
VALLEY

Frank C. Laubach
Elizabeth Mooney Kirk
Robert S. Laubach

Correlated reader to accompany
Skill Book 1: Sounds and Names of Letters

New Readers Press   •   Syracuse, New York

1. Uncle Ted visits Indian Valley

This is Indian Valley.
Mr. Glenn Hill lives in Indian Valley.
Mrs. Glenn Hill lives in Indian Valley.
Kim and Jill live in Indian Valley.
Ed lives in Indian Valley.
The Hills live in Indian Valley.

Uncle Ted is visiting Indian Valley.

Fran and Van are visiting Indian Valley.

Uncle Ted puts up a tent at the river.

Uncle Ted is at the tent.

Fran and Van are at the tent.

Uncle Ted picks apples in the valley.

Fran and Van pick apples in the valley.

Uncle Ted puts his apples in a box.

Fran puts her apples in a box.

Van puts his apples in a box.

Two boys are looking at the apples.
Van has an apple in his hand.
He gives his apple to one boy.
Fran has an apple in her hand.
She gives her apple to one boy.
The boys thank Van and Fran.

Van puts ten apples in a dish.
He visits the Hills.
He gives the ten apples to Mrs. Hill.
Mrs. Hill thanks him for the apples.

2. Ned gets a fish

Snake River is in the valley.

Fish are in Snake River.

The fish are jumping.

Ned Oliver is looking at the fish.

A man is fishing in Snake River.

Ned is looking at the man.

The man has three fish.
He puts the fish in a box.
Ned gives the man a quarter.
The man gives Ned a fish.
Ned has the fish in his hand.
The man has the quarter in his hand.

Ned gives the fish to Mrs. Oliver.
She thanks him for the fish.
She puts the fish in a pan.

3. Uncle Ted and the snake

Ed and Robert are in the valley.
Van and Fran are in the valley.
The children are looking at a bird.
They are looking at the bird's wings.
They are looking at the bird's eggs.

The bird's eggs are in a nest.
Three eggs are in the bird's nest.
The bird is on the nest.
The eggs are under the bird's wings.

The children run to the river.
Uncle Ted is at the river.
Van yells to Uncle Ted,
"Look at the bird's nest!
Three eggs are in the nest."

Fran says, "The bird is on the nest.
The eggs are under the bird's wings."

Uncle Ted looks at the nest.
The bird is not on the nest.
Two eggs are in the nest.
One egg is not in the nest.
The children look for the egg.

Robert jumps and yells,
"A snake, a snake!
Look at the snake.
The snake has the egg.
The snake has the bird's egg."

The four children jump and yell.
Ed says, "The snake has the bird's egg.
Uncle Ted, look at the snake.
Look! The snake is going to the river.
The snake lives in the river."

The snake is going to the river.
The snake is in the river.
The snake lives in the river.

4. Mr. and Mrs. Hill visit Sam's shop

This is Sam's shop.

The shop is in the valley.

Sam sells fish and apples in his shop.

He sells eggs and olives in his shop.

He sells zippers in his shop.

He sells cups and pans in his shop.

Mr. and Mrs. Hill are in the shop.
Glenn Hill gets olives for Jill.
He gets a cup for Ed.
Liz Hill gets a dish for Kim.
She gets a zipper for Jill.
She gets a pan for Uncle Ted.

Liz gives Sam ten quarters.
One quarter is for the cup.
One quarter is for the dish.
One quarter is for the zipper.
Three quarters are for the olives.
Four quarters are for the pan.

Sam thanks Liz for the ten quarters.

14

Glenn tells Sam,
"The olives are for Jill.
The zipper is for Jill.
The dish is for Kim.
The cup is for Ed.
The pan is for my uncle.
He is visiting in the valley."

5. The pup is hurt

A pup is under the shop.
Mr. Hill gets the pup.
He pets the pup.
He looks at the pup's leg.
The pup's leg is hurt.

Mr. Hill gives the pup to Ed.
Mr. Hill tells Ed,
"This pup is hurt.
The pup's leg is hurt."

Ed tells Mr. Hill,
"This is Robert Oliver's pup.
This is Robert's pup Queen.
Robert is at the river.
He is looking for Queen."

Mr. Hill tells Ed,
"Run to the river.
Give Queen to Robert."

Ed runs to the river.
Ed yells,
"Look, Robert!
I have Queen.
Her leg is hurt."

Ed gives the pup to Robert.
Robert pets his pup.
Robert tells Ed,
"Thanks, Ed."

6. Uncle Ted visits Ann and Cal

Uncle Ted is at the river.
A woman and her boy are at the river.

The woman says, "I am Ann Bird.
This is my boy.
His name is Cal.
Cal and I live in Indian Valley.
Do you live in the valley?"

Uncle Ted says, "No, I do not.
I am visiting the Hills.
I am Ted Hill.
I am Glenn Hill's uncle.
I have a pet shop on York Street."

Cal says, "A pet shop!
I have pets.
I have two pups."

Uncle Ted says, "I sell fish.
I sell pups and birds."

Cal says, "Do you sell snakes?"

Uncle Ted says, "Yes, I do."

Cal says, "I have three snakes."

Uncle Ted visits Ann and Cal.
They live at 9 Valley Street.
Uncle Ted looks at Cal's snakes.
Cal sells one snake to Uncle Ted.

Uncle Ted says,
"The snake is for my pet shop."

Uncle Ted picks up the snake.
He puts the snake in a box.

Uncle Ted says, "Thank you for the snake.
Thank you, Cal and Ann."
He gives his telephone number to Ann and Cal.
His telephone number is 745-4938.

They give their telephone number to him.
Their telephone number is 234-8571.

7. Uncle Ted packs up

Uncle Ted is packing.
Fran and Van are packing.
Uncle Ted packs the pans in a box.
Van packs the cups in a box.

Fran picks up the box of pans.
Van picks up the box of cups.
Mr. Hill picks up the box of apples.
Uncle Ted picks up the tent.

Uncle Ted is going to York Street.
Fran and Van are going to York Street.

This is Indian Valley.
The river is in Indian Valley.
The fish are in the river.
The birds are in the valley.
The Hills are in the valley.
Uncle Ted is not in the valley.
Fran and Van are not in the valley.

Word list

In the Valley, the correlated reader for Skill Book 1:
Sounds and Names of Letters, introduces the 13 new
words listed below. The 18 variants of words introduced
in Skill Book 1 are also listed.

New word	Page	Variant	Page
am	19	apples	6
hurt	16	bird's	10
nest	11	Cal's	20
of	22	cups	13
packing	22	give	17
packs	22	Hill's	20
tells	15	jump	12
ten	7	looks	11
under	11	olives	13
visit	13	pans	13
visiting	6	pick	6
visits	5	quarters	14
wings	10	Robert's	17
		run	11
		sell	20
		thanks	7
		yell	12
		zippers	13

DISCARDED

24